Measuring Maintenance Workforce Productivity made simple

Stephen J. Thomas

Measuring Maintenance Workforce Productivity Made Simple
Stephen J. Thomas
ISBN 978-0-9825163-8-6

Publisher: Terrence O'Hanlon
Page Layout and Cover Design: Patricia Serio

For information: Reliabilityweb.com
www.reliabilityweb.com
PO Box 60075, Ft. Myers, FL 33906
Toll Free: 888-575-1245 | Phone: 239-333-2500
E-mail: customerservice@reliabilityweb.com

10 9 8 7 6 5 4 3 2 1

TABLE OF CONTENTS

Introduction vii

Chapter 1: Improving Productivity Through Work Sampling 1
1.1 Insight 1
1.2 The Purpose of Work Sampling 2
1.3 What is Work Sampling? 3
1.4 Two Approaches to the Problem 5
1.5 Advantages to the In-House Approach 6
1.6 Category Definitions 8
1.7 Factors Affecting Validity 11
1.8 Productivity Factor 14
1.9 Breaking Down Management's Resistance 16

Chapter 2: The Planning Phase 19
2.1 The Process 19
2.2 Roles and Responsibilities 19
2.3 Preparation Activities – The Checklist 23
2.4 The Process Timetable 25
2.5 The Survey Duration 26
2.6 How To Set Up Random Foremen Selection 27
2.7 Description of the Training Process 29

Chapter 3: The Execution Phase 33
3.1 Sampling Methodology 33
3.2 Rules for Work Sampling 33
3.3 Typical Problems and What to Do About Them 34

3.4 Process Monitoring....36

Chapter 4: The Results Phase....39
4.1 What Do You Do With the Data?....39
4.2 The Work Sampling Charts....41
4.3 Additional Views....42
4.4 Now That You Have the Data, What's Next?....42
4.5 Now That You Understand the Roots, What's Next?....44

Chapter 5: The Continuous Improvement Phase....45
5.1 Over and Over Again....45
5.2 When to Resample....45

Chapter 6: Spot Sampling....47
6.1 Spot Sampling....47
6.2 Site Commitment and the Spot Audit Team....48
6.3 Resource Requirements....49
6.4 The Process....50
6.5 Actions Items/Analysis....51

From the Author....53

Appendix....55
1. Work Sampling Form....56
2. Spot Audit Form....57
3. Sample Charts....58
3.1 Direct Work Sample Chart....58
3.2 Indirect Work Sample Chart....59
3.3 Non-Productive Sample Chart....60
3.4 Sample Count Chart....61
3.5 Samples Per Period....62

Bibliography....63

About the Author....65

Introduction

Let me ask you a question: Why would you undertake a work initiative if you had no way to measure its success? The answer is that you probably wouldn't want to work in this fashion. Unfortunately, this is something that takes place more often than not in the maintenance work arena. We develop and implement many initiatives to improve how the work is conducted, but when it comes to checking on the success of these initiatives we are often at a loss as to how to accomplish this task. The reason the majority of the initiatives developed are designed is to improve productivity of the workforce, yet we find it difficult to find ways to measure worker productivity effectively over time.

There are many answers to the question posed by management, "How do we measure productivity?" There are consultant-focused solutions as well as those that can be accomplished internally. There are complex work-study processes, and those that are not so complex. Each of these approaches will deliver an answer to the productivity question posed by management. The question: Which one to choose?

My approach in this text is to provide you with a process that is:

- Easy to use
- Easy to understand
- Easy to implement
- Engages the workforce

- Low-to-no cost
- Can be replicated over time to track continuous improvement, and
- With slight modification, can be applied to virtually any size organization

The reasoning behind the need to deliver on these criteria is simply that we need a tool that enables us to track productivity improvement over time and assure ourselves that the initiatives we employ are adding business value.

Chapter 1: Improving Productivity Through Work Sampling

1.1 Insight

Maintenance organizations are continuously making improvements in how they execute their work. Improvements in work planning and scheduling, job preparation, material acquisition and staging, as well as other facets of the total job are the norm. The question that needs to be asked and answered is, how do you know if all of these improvements are working and making the organization more productive? After all that is what each one of these initiatives is designed to accomplish.

The manner in which you can determine if your efforts are delivering value is to accurately measure workforce productivity over time, recognize and applaud the improvements, and take corrective action to address areas where the process has not delivered as expected. This process is most often referred to as work sampling, and if done correctly, the effort can provide you with the measurements to clearly determine if your efforts are delivering the value expected.

If you asked a cross section of the management team at your plant site what they believed was the percentage of time in a day that a worker was productive, you would get a wide variety of answers ranging from very low to very high. Unfortunately these answers are subjective and most often have little basis in fact. They are what we refer to as a "gut feel" about the level of actual work that a typical mechanic can accomplish in a day. In addition, if you look at specific tasks and observe the workforce, you would find that everyone's estimate of productivity is probably correct, but only within a narrow and limited view.

What we need to do is to develop a methodology that enables us to measure productivity in a way that is comprehensive, consistent, statistically accurate, replicable, and engages the entire workforce. We need a process that is viewed as adding value, and not one of management checking up with punishment of the slackers to follow.

This form of measurement and the associated corrective action will over time enable you to add significant value to the business. In addition, you will know what parts of the maintenance work process are functioning well and which require additional attention. In other words, you will be engaged in delivering the improvements needed to help optimize workforce productivity.

1.2 The Purpose of Work Sampling

I would venture a guess that the vast majority of people come to work every day with the expressed desire to do a good day's work. The problem is that barriers get in the way, most of which are not the fault of the workforce. The purpose of work sampling is to gather data that clearly indicates how the maintenance workforce is utilized during the workday. The results from this review can be analyzed and work process problems addressed in order to correct deficiencies. The objective is to identify the barriers and break them down, not just once, but forever!

A work sampling review also provides measured, statistically accurate data that can be used as a benchmark for future studies. Doing a single study is like trying to draw a line with only one data point. It cannot be done. You need multiple points to draw the line and similarly, you need multiple studies taken over time to show improvement as well as to show the areas that require corrective action. In this manner, you can determine if the implemented work process strategies have been successful.

Quite often when a company thinks about trying to measure workforce productivity, they run into problems that often stop the effort before it can even get started. First, when they do some research into the amount of effort required, they are overwhelmed by the time required, the cost, and often just the complexity of the effort. Second, if a company engages a contractor to perform the study, there are additional drawbacks including the cost, problems with the workforce's perception of the reason for the effort, and the ability of the contractor to measure progress over time without additional cost to the company.

I believe that a process can be put in place that can be accomplished internally at low-to-no cost and will yield results that will enable a company to measure productivity and validate their efforts to improve it.

1.3 What is Work Sampling?

Work sampling is a measurement technique based on a random sampling of the workforce to determine what types of activities they are performing over the course of the day. Having productivity-related information is invaluable. It provides data that shows when the workforce is and is not being productive. Additionally, in the non-productive times, it provides insight into what is getting in the way of the work.

Work sampling is not a measure of work efficiency. It will not tell you if the work is being done correctly or in the time estimated for its completion, but it will tell you if the workforce is engaged in actual "hands-on" work.

It is based upon the theory that a limited set of samples taken at random from a large group will have the same pattern of distribution as the large group. If the survey sample is large enough, the characteristics of the sample will differ little from those of the group, and thereby allow for analysis of the large group using only a small yet significant sample of data.

The important aspect of all of this is the sample size. The exact degree of accuracy of a sampling study can be regulated by varying the number of observations taken. To arrive at the proper number of samples to reach statistical accuracy the following formula can be applied:

$$E = +/- 2 * \sqrt{\frac{P\ (1-P)}{N}}$$

E = Absolute error

P = Percent observations in the Productive Category

N = Total number of observations

You don't need to spend time working out the details of this formula. The goal for reasonable statistical accuracy is +/- 2.5%. The above equation is not only dependent on the number of observations, but also dependent on the percent of observations in the productivity category. Therefore, based on an assumed productivity of the workforce the number of samples needed can be calculated. The bottom line is that for a current productivity level ranging between 25% and 45% (industry normal range) you need about 2000 sample points to obtain statistically valid data. This may seem like a lot but as you will see, it really is not that many and not as difficult to acquire as you may think.

For those of you with small workforces, do not be dismayed. While it is difficult to acquire the needed sample size, you can also be effective doing a spot sampling at the beginning of the workday. This effort is described in detail in Chapter 6. Spot auditing also works well for larger organizations, but it is only a subset of the full-blown assessment and to really improve, I suggest that you do the full-blown work sampling first. The reason is that when you do a full-blown work sampling you learn about productivity issues that exist throughout the entire day while a spot audit only focuses on a single time period.

1.4 Two Approaches to the Problem

There are two approaches to conducting a work sampling activity. Each has positive and negative aspects and these need consideration prior to embarking on the effort.

The first approach is to contract the entire process. With this approach, all of the work is turned over to a consultant. This includes setup, sampling, recording, and reporting the results. The upside of this approach is that a company with expertise in work sampling will do the work for you and provide you with the resultant data and analysis. The downside to this strategy is that the site personnel do not own the process. As a result, they will probably not take ownership of the output of the sampling assessment especially if the results are not favorable. Another problem with this approach is that the consultant takes on the role of a third-party observer. This role has many negative connotations with the workforce (mechanics and foremen) since many may interpret it as "spying for management." This severely undermines any value that this effort is designed to accomplish. Last but not least is that this approach is expensive not only the first time but also every other time that you want to do follow-up studies.

The other approach is to have the site personnel take ownership of the entire process with a consultant possibly acting in the role of advisor or assistant. The work process that will be described throughout this text addresses this approach. It involves the site appointing a site champion, a coordinator, and doing the actual survey work with the supervision in the plant. This eliminates the "observer/spy" syndrome usually associated with consultants doing the sampling. It closely ties the foremen into the process since they are the ones who are making the observations. This strategy also ties the site personnel into the results because they are the ones who indirectly provide the data. The ability to skew the data on a limited basis is present, but the number of foremen, the number of samples, and the random nature of the process make this nearly impossible.

In the approach where the site owns the process, a work sampling trained consultant may take on the role of behind-the-scenes assistant to make sure that the process works correctly. I do not believe that this is really needed, but the first time that you do a work sampling it may be worthwhile. The only possible problem is that the consultant's methods may be different from what I describe. In that case, you will need to have them align their support with your process for the sake of consistency not just for the initial study, but for all those you will conduct in the future.

1.5 Advantages to the In-House Approach

I believe strongly in what I refer to as the in-house approach. For that reason, the remainder of this text is going to focus on that aspect of work sampling. Consultants will tell you that based on their experience doing the work they can add more value in a shorter time frame. In many cases, this is true, but it is very expensive and often builds no ownership to a process that must be more than a one-time event if it truly is going to be worthwhile.

My rationale for strongly supporting the in-house effort is based on the following reasons:

- Economics – It may be worthwhile to engage a consultant to conduct a work-study if all that you want is a "one-time" snapshot of the productivity level of the workforce. However, that brings us back to the concept of trying to draw a line with only one reference point. It does not work. What you need to really understand workforce productivity and determine if you are eliminating work barriers, is repeated studies over time. While this can be handled by a consultant, it truly can be an expensive proposition and one which most management organizations lose interest in over time.

- Perception – Productivity studies have a negative connotation with the workforce as well as management at the front line and with other levels within the organization. There is a belief that bad things follow a study of this nature such as reorganization and layoff. This is certainly not the case with true work sampling. What you are really trying to do is identify barriers to productivity and then eliminate them. Bringing in a consultant to handle the task reduces or even eliminates buy-in and invariably will generate resistance to virtually any changes proposed.

- Buy-in – If done correctly work-studies take place at predetermined time intervals, for example, every six months. The purpose is to clearly determine if the productivity changes made in the work process are successful in eliminating barriers to accomplishing the work. To have this type of work process embedded in the organization you need buy-in at all levels. People need to understand why the studies are being conducted and what is being done with the results. This is somewhat difficult to accomplish with a third party since they are most often viewed as outsiders.

- Group learning – Along with buy-in comes a very important aspect of change—learning from what you have done and making it better in the future. With an engaged workforce this is a strong possibility. The majority of people would like to come to work to do a day's work and not be impeded by productivity barriers.

- Accuracy – The in-house approach provides a high degree of statistical accuracy based on the number of samples that will be taken. Obtaining the sample level needed is accomplished with little expense when the study is done in-house. This is not the case with the contractor approach. Most organizations do not want to spend large amounts of money doing work sampling. They want the result but at a reasonable cost. Consequently, they do not expect a contractor conducting a sampling project to be on site full-time for long periods. To address this problem, the contractors approach the work sampling problem in a different manner to obtain sample data in a short (less expensive) time period. This is accomplished by taking "snapshots" of the work or embedding themselves in a work group for a period of time. My contention is that while the contractor will provide a reasonable report in this fashion, the amount of data by which they draw their conclusions is not extensive enough to state that the entire organization has encountered the barriers that they have identified.

- Replication – Handling the work sampling effort in-house allows the organization to become familiar with how the process is conducted and be able to replicate it repeatedly as work productivity improvement is tracked. This is important because work sampling is not a one-time event.

1.6 Category Definitions

An important aspect of work sampling is the categories that identify what the workforce was doing at the time the samples were taken. This data when compiled provides a statistically accurate picture in three main categories: direct work, indirect work, and work which is non-productive. For this reason, it is very important that everyone involved—those sampling and those being sampled—understand the definitions. A universal understanding will go a long away in support of the effort by making certain that everything is categorized correctly. The descriptions of each major category and their subcategories follow:

Direct Work

Workers engaged in this category are directly involved with the actual work. There are two subcategories that define this aspect:

- Working – In the working category, the mechanics are actually applying physical effort to a tool or material in order to accomplish the job. It is also recommended that handling tools or materials within 75′ of the job site, safety, standby, and "hole watch" on towers are also considered in the working category. For the visual observation part of the sampling effort, recognizing the working category is relatively simple.

- Planning – Not all direct work is associated with holding a tool and applying physical effort. There is a planning aspect of the work in which the mechanic is doing things that are associated with planning the actual job required for the completion of the work. Examples would be: planning job steps with another mechanic; sketching; reading a print; measuring; layout; and other tasks that directly support the work effort.

Indirect Work

Workers involved in indirect activities are doing things that support those directly working or will support those in the indirect category when they begin the actual job. As with the working category, these tasks are easy to recognize by the person collecting the sample data.

- Receiving Instructions – The mechanic is discussing the overall job (different from planning job steps in the working category) or receiving instruction from a supervisor or foreman.

- Job Safety Issues – This category involves all safety related issues such as: job review with operations/production; safety; standby instruction; or any other aspects of the work directly related to safely performing the job.

- Handling Tools – Every job requires tools of some sort. This category addresses the procurement of tools for the job or the return of tools following job completion.

- Handling Material – This category applies the same criteria we applied in the handling tools category except in this case we are referring to the procurement of job related material.
- Handling Equipment – Much of the equipment used on a job requires some level of setup as well as breakdown at the end of a job. Often this effort is minor such as positioning a welding machine and attaching the leads. In other cases, it is far from minor such as setting up a large crane with counterweights which can take days to complete.
- Clean-up – Last but not the least part of any job is clean-up. Cleaning up the job site following work completion also falls into the indirect category because as we all know, "No job is really completed until it is cleaned up."

Non-Productive Work

This category is designed to capture all of the time in the day when no work is being performed (direct or indirect). These categories are relatively self-explanatory and are also easily identified by those doing the sampling. They include:

- Waiting for Tools – Waiting for tools is different from handling tools and usually applies to waiting on tool delivery for specialty items that may need to be ordered from the tool room or moved to the job from another location in the plant. It may even apply to waiting for tool delivery from an outside vendor.
- Waiting for Materials – The ideal situation (one that often does not exist) is that all materials are at the job site when the work is ready to start. When this condition does not exist, the materials need to be ordered either through the on-site storeroom or

possibly through a third party. In any case, the work cannot proceed and the mechanics need to wait for delivery.

- Waiting for Permits – Most jobs cannot be started without a permit provided usually from the safety or production departments. If the work is well planned, the permit delay is usually short. However, if the planning was not handled correctly or if the permit writers are busy there may be a significant (non-productive) delay.
- Waiting Other – This is a "catch all" category where the mechanics are required to wait for reasons not included in the more definitive categories above.
- Traveling – Plants vary in size. Some only require that the work crew walk to the job, usually a short distance away from their staging area. Others are spread out over large geographical areas and require travel time to get to and from the job site. This category covers traveling that is not job related. For example, this would include time to and from breaks, and starts and quits at the beginning and end of the day respectively. Travel for the job would be covered as an indirect item depending on why the travel was required.
- Lost Time – This last category includes items that do not fit other categories such as safety meetings, lunch, other meetings, smoke breaks, and other times where the mechanics are off the job for nonwork issues.

1.7 Factors Affecting Validity

When the idea of in-house work sampling is brought to the attention of management the immediate concern is one of the validity of the samples taken. There are several factors that affect the validity of the results. These are addressed in how the process is configured and most importantly, the communication provided to those involved as to the purpose of the sampling and what will be done with the results.

Configuration

How the process is configured is critical for success and has the following components:

- Instantaneous Observation – The process needs to be set up so that sampling by the observer is relatively instantaneous. There should be no attempt to anticipate or generalize the activities being performed. The observers need to make their best effort to understand what is going on at the job site and properly classify the observation based on the categories already discussed. This is why frontline supervisors are employed.
- Randomness – The randomness of the sampling process must be insured if the data is to be valid. The use of a random process to select observers and time slots for the observations will ensure that this takes place. This will be discussed when I describe how to set up the work sampling event.
- Sample Duration – Not only does the effort require instantaneous and random observation, but it also needs to be of short duration. To accomplish this, the supervisor will have fifteen minutes to sample the entire crew. The reason behind this is that we want to know what people are doing at a point in time, and a fifteen-minute period for an entire crew provides this data.
- Sample Size – The number of observations made is dependent on the perceived percentage in the working category and the required degree of survey accuracy. As previously mentioned the sample size needs to be 2000 or more for a decent level of statistical

accuracy. Acquiring the needed sample size is not as difficult a task as you may think. Since sampling efforts run for several weeks, let us assume that you have a maintenance organization of fifty mechanics. Two samples per day for each over a five-day week is 500 samples and over four weeks, 2000.

Bias

Bias is a problem that must be addressed if our efforts are to provide valid information. The way we will go about minimizing bias is through open and honest communication as to the purpose of the effort and what will be done with the results. If people understand why the effort is being undertaken and do not feel threatened by the outcome, they will work very hard to eliminate bias and provide accurate sample data. After all, improved working conditions are something that everyone is interested in acquiring. The two types of bias we need to eliminate are:

- Bias by the Observer – The most significant potential bias problem is that of the observer. Unless the observers understand and buy into the process there is the likelihood that they may bias their observations toward the working category. This problem can be overcome through upfront communication by the management team. The other good news is that due to the large number of random samples, the bias is virtually eliminated. In other words, a single person cannot bias the data sufficiently to undermine the effort.

- Bias by Those Observed – The entire organization must fully understand the purpose and goals of the study. It is critical that the observed activity accurately represents what is really taking place at the work site if valid results are to be obtained.

1.8 Productivity Factor

The Productivity Factor is an attempt to portray or normalize the overall level of workforce productivity by a single number taking into account the differences between sites. This serves a specific purpose. It allows for the productivity levels from various sites within a single company, or sites across companies, to be compared even though they may have different configurations.

The Productivity Factor is represented by the following equation:

Y = (A+.075A+T)*(100+X)

- **Y** = Productivity Factor (%)
- **A** = Average Productivity for the Study (%)
- **.075A** = Supplemental Allowance (%)
- **T** = Travel Allowance (%)
- **X** = Personal Fatigue Allowance (%)

Average Productivity (A) is the total percent of the samples in the Direct Work categories which includes both Working and Planning.

Supplemental Allowance (.075A) takes into consideration the supplemental contribution of the Indirect categories as an important part of work. While it is not actual work unto itself it contributes to getting work accomplished. Therefore 7.5% of A (Average Productivity) is added to the total workforce productivity.

Travel Allowance (T) recognizes that workers often need to travel as an integral part of accomplishing work. This is most often determined by the size of the plant. For this reason a small percent is added into the calculation of overall productivity per the table.

Type of Site	Description	Added "T" Value
Compact Site	The plant site resides within an area of one square mile or less and is not separated by obstacles such as roads or railroads.	1.0%
Semi-Compact	The plant site resides within an area of greater than one square mile and is not separated by obstacles such as roads or railroads.	1.2%
Natural Obstacle	The plant has areas separated by natural obstacles such as railroads, major highways, etc.	1.3%
Separated Site	The plant has a physical separation which requires workers to travel a distance between these areas to conduct the work.	1.5%

Personal Fatigue Allowance (X) provides for personal needs and fatigue. The higher the level of productivity the greater the allowance added into the formula. The correlation is that the harder people work the higher the level of fatigue and need to rest which should not be treated wholly as non-productive time. The table created for this follows:

Productivity %	"X" Value
0% to 20%	6%
21% to 40%	8%
41% to 60%	10%
61% to 80%	12%
81% to 100%	15%

An example of the calculation of the Productivity Factor (Y) follows for a plant with 38% as the estimated average score in the direct category and no travel allowance:

Y = (A+.075A+T)*(100+X)

A = 38%

.075A = 38*.075 = 2.85%

T = 1% (based on the table)

X = 8% (based on the table)

Y = (38+2.85+1)*(100+8)

Y = (41.85)*1.08

Y = 45.19

1.9 Breaking Down Management's Resistance

The first chapter would not be complete unless we briefly touched on management's resistance to the in-house approach. For some reason many management teams seem to believe that either the sampling process is too difficult to be handled in-house or that the results obtained from their own employees would be less than accurate. In order to gain permission to proceed you need to dispel both of these serious misconceptions.

It's Too Difficult

As you hopefully have learned as you have read through Chapter 1, it really isn't difficult at all. It involves a large number of random samples which eliminates any possible bias and provides you with a high degree of statistically accurate data concerning your workforce's productivity level.

People Will Provide Inaccurate Data Invalidating the Effort

This is only true if you allow it to happen. If open and honest communication about the purpose behind the sampling and what will be done with the results is provided upfront to your organization then there should be no reason why anyone would try to make it fail. The key is in your convincing the management team that this is a viable low-cost method for acquiring some very important information.

How do you go about this task? The answer is to convince them to allow you to conduct a pilot effort. This would entail conducting a short duration sampling effort in one specific area of the plant. All you need, as you shall see in later chapters, is a clerk and a way to contact the supervisors involved. There is no other cost except maybe your time to assemble the information into a presentable form. How can someone turn down the ability to obtain productivity data for free? If you can get the management team to let you conduct a pilot effort then the results should sell the program.

Chapter 2: The Planning Phase

2.1 The Process

The work sampling process is simple. It is conducted by the foremen who directly supervise the workforce. After all, they know what their crews are supposed to be doing and when they make their observations, they have the distinct ability of being the most accurate.

To properly gather the data samples, a random selection process will be established with the foreman being assigned to sample their crews when contacted by the coordinator. This contact will be made five to ten minutes before their fifteen minute survey time. For example a designated foreman would be contacted at 8:50 a.m. and told that their sample time was from 9:00 to 9:15 a.m. The foreman would then sample his crew during that time frame making one "point-in-time" observation for each person. He would then fill out the survey sheet indicating the number of people in his work group that fell into each of the categories. The notations will be numbers of people—no names! This sheet will then be turned into the coordinator the same day for entry into the database. The goal is to not have the foreman do sampling more than twice per day. The work sampling form is provided in the appendix.

2.2 Roles and Responsibilities

Every work effort that has ever been successful has had a group of people who are involved in the effort and "clearly" understand their roles and responsibilities. There are four key roles in the process and one additional one if you are going to use a consultant in a supporting function. They are as follows:

Site Management

As with every effort, the involvement and support of the site managerial team is critical. If the leadership team does not make this an important part of the business the effort is doomed before you even begin. People take their direction from leadership whether it is through direct work assignment or on a more subtle level, by watching what the leaders consider important and then acting on those items. The site management team needs to support the effort in both word and deed. They need to be part of the upfront presentation to the organization so that everyone will know that they consider it an important effort and why. They also need to be a part of the effort as it progresses asking questions along the way to assure that it is healthy and proceeding on course. A weekly meeting with the site champion is appropriate so that they can stay in touch as well as provide support where and when it is needed.

The Site Champion

The site champion is the point person for the effort. In the planning phase the work required is going to take up a good portion of the person's time. After all, if you plan something well then the execution phase is less fraught with problems. However, after the process gets going the workload will only be part-time since the effort is really being handled by the coordinator and the foreman. The main responsibilities of the site champion include:

- He is the identified process owner and is accountable to management for the execution of the initiative. Acting as a single point contact enables him to work at all levels within the organization to make the effort a success.

- It is the responsibility of the site champion to handle the communication process. It is an undeniable truth that "perception is reality." Good communication throughout the entire effort will help everyone understand what is taking place as well as why it is being done. If you want buy-in and success, communication is a key element.

- The site champion also needs to develop the training, schedule the attendance and most important of all make certain that the management team attends. It is his responsibility to explain why the sampling is being conducted as well as what he plans to do with the results.

- In plants that are unionized, the site champion needs to work with the management team to make certain that the union understands what is being done and why. Different plants have different union-management relationships and this part of the effort needs to be carefully handled so that the work sampling study receives union support. That is not to say that in the majority of the cases it cannot proceed without union support, but having them on board and visibly supportive is the better option. Sharing the results and corrective actions associated with the effort is often a good approach to get the union to buy in.

- As the data is reported by the foremen, it is the responsibility of the site champion to monitor the data to make certain it is accurate and being submitted in a timely manner. This enables the site champion stay in close contact with the foremen/samplers so that they can gain a clear understanding of what is and is not working. Having this information will allow adjustments to the process if needed.

- The last responsibility of the site champion is to generate the random sampling list on a weekly basis. Random samples are a critical component of the effort and will be discussed in a later section.

The Coordinator

The coordinator position has two responsibilities. They maintain the random sample list and make the contact with the foremen ten minutes before the sampling period. The follow-up step in the process is for the coordinator to make certain that they receive the data and enter it into the spreadsheet that is used for logging the sample data. One would hope that this would be a simple task but it often isn't as simple as we would like it to be. At times, foremen cannot be contacted or do not turn in the survey cards. In these cases the coordinator has to track down the people to keep the process moving. This is the one job that can become full-time during the sampling period if things are not working smoothly.

The Supervisor/Foremen

The role of the foremen is the most critical part of the effort. They are the data gatherers and without this part of the process functioning well there is no work sampling. For that reason it is vitally important that the foremen understand why the sampling is being conducted and their role in the process.

The data-gathering effort is relatively simple and doesn't require much effort. Of all people, the foremen know where their crews are located and what they are supposed to be doing at any given time. The problem is that the sampling is based on random time slots and the foremen may be doing something else when they are contacted for their sample. By understanding the importance of their role they will appreciate the need to stop whatever it is they are doing and conduct the sample in the assigned time period. This can be further supported by management during training and by the site champion as they interact with the foremen during the effort.

The other important part of the foremen's job is to submit their survey cards as soon as possible. This eliminates possible loss of the data as well as giving the coordinator time to make the entries.

The Consultant

You may choose not to use a consultant in this effort since the vast majority want to convince you to allow them to do the work for you. However, there are those out there who will take on a "backseat" advisory role and help you achieve your goals. If you can find a consultant who fits this role you may want to consider using them for the first sampling. The value inherent in this approach is that they can help you over the rough spots and enable you to avoid problems that you might not otherwise identify early in the effort. They can also provide you with their own experiences that will help to make the effort better than it would be if done completely in-house.

The important thing to remember is that work sampling is something that you are going to be doing periodically as you measure productivity over time. You need to take ownership of the effort otherwise when the consultant leaves, the process leaves with them.

2.3 Preparation Activities – The Checklist

If you have gotten this far you have convinced your site management team that work sampling is something that can add value to the business by improving workforce productivity. The next step is to develop a checklist to get you from where you are to the starting point of the effort.

The Checklist (Things to think about/Things to remember to do)

- ☐ Identify the site champion
- ☐ Train the site champion

  - ☐ Work sampling information
  - ☐ Work sampling process
  - ☐ How to monitor the process
- ☐ Union discussion and training (if required)
- ☐ Communication with the organization (why the survey is being conducted and what will be done with the results)
- ☐ Decide when to start the survey
- ☐ Determine what crafts will be sampled (suggestion: do the full workforce)
- ☐ Determine the number of data points (this will determine the survey duration)
- ☐ Obtain site specific information related to the daily schedule of the workforce (needed for timing)
  - ☐ Start time
  - ☐ Quit time
  - ☐ Lunch
  - ☐ Breaks
  - ☐ Number of foremen who will participate
- ☐ Set up the weekly random sampling table based on foremen and data required
- ☐ Identify and train the site coordinator
- ☐ Identify a back-up coordinator
- ☐ Prepare the training material (one hour needed for the foremen)
- ☐ Arrange for the training room
- ☐ Handouts for those who will be in training
- ☐ Site manager – opening remarks
- ☐ Site champion to conduct training
- ☐ Develop the process for turning in data cards after sampling
- ☐ Conduct training
- ☐ Build the database/matrix to record data (Excel is a good format)
- ☐ Start the effort

2.4 The Process Timetable

The timetable shown below is designed to give you some idea of the time required to get ready to start. Quite honestly it is "fast track" and based on other things that are going on at your site and with prior time commitments, it probably will take longer. Nevertheless it does help you sequence the tasks; those that are strategic and those that are tactical.

Timing	Strategic	Tactical
Week 1–2	• Management team discussion and agreement to conduct the study • Communication with site personnel. Face-to-face communication is the best way. Avoid memos and e-mails.	• Determine a start date so that you have a deadline to work toward.
Week 3	• Appoint the site champion • Union discussion (if required) • Determine strategy to obtain significant number of samples • Determine what crafts will be surveyed (suggest all)	• Determine site coordinator and arrange logistics • Coordinator begins development of random survey process and spreadsheet for logging data
Week 4–5	• Training for foremen (should be done by site manager and site champion) • Communication to all site personnel	• Prepare forms/ distribute • Communicate • Finalize process for handling survey data

(Continued)

Week 6–??	• Monitor process and take corrective action as needed	• Survey/submit data to coordinator.
Week ??	• Develop and present final report • Communicate findings to organization	• Survey ends. Schedule next survey in approximately 6 months. • Develop and implement corrective actions based on survey results

2.5 The Survey Duration

The sampling effort needs to be as long as needed to obtain the required number of work samples over all of the sample time slots. Remember, we said that about 2000 samples would provide a good statistical representation of workforce productivity but upwards of 5000 would give you even more data points per time slot and somewhat more detailed information.

The duration really depends on the number of samples you want to obtain and how many foremen you have in your organization. We don't want to overburden the foremen so two random samples per day is probably enough.

Form for Determining the Duration (in weeks):		
A	Enter the number of foremen to sampled	
B	Number of samples per day	2
C	Enter the average crew size	
D	Samples/day = A × B × C	
E	Days/week	5
F	Samples/week = D × E	
G	# of weeks for 2000 samples = 2000/F	

Using the preceding chart you can easily figure out how many weeks you will need to sample to get to the statistically accurate 2000 minimum sample level. The real governing criterion is the size of the organization. For large organizations, obtaining the needed sample size is relatively easy and serious consideration should be given for targeting a sample set greater than 2000. But what if you are a small organization with few foremen and a small workforce? Unfortunately in this situation obtaining a large sample set is going to take time. You have two choices: Take the time you need to get the results, or go to Chapter 6. This chapter addresses what is referred to as spot job audits and may help you improve your productivity without an extended sampling period. For those of you with large organizations, we will discuss spot job audits as another way of obtaining data, but please don't use it exclusively and abandon the full sampling effort.

2.6 How To Set Up Random Foremen Selection

It is important that each of the foremen is selected randomly throughout the day for them to sample their crews. There are all sorts of ways to accomplish setting up the schedule. One of the simplest ways is to identify the start and quit times for the workforce. Next, break each day down into fifteen-minute increments (the sampling periods). This should give you a spreadsheet with the days (Monday through Friday) across the top and the time increments in a vertical column on the left. As an example, let's assume the crews work from 7:00 a.m. to 3:30 p.m. with one half hour off for lunch. Your spreadsheet would look like the one on the following page.

	Monday	Tuesday	Wednesday	Thursday	Friday
7:00–7:15					
7:15–7:30					
7:30–7:45					
7:45–8:00					
8:00–8:15					
(For the sake of space, the full day is not shown)					
3:00–3:15					
3:15–3:30					

First, we will not sample during the lunch period since we already know where everyone is going to be located. Therefore for an eight-hour day, there will be thirty-two 15-minute slots to fill with a foreman's name. Unless you have sixteen foremen you can quickly see that every slot will not get sampled every day.

The next step is very unscientific. For each day of the week (you will be developing the random schedule one week at a time) create a sheet with the time slots listed down the left hand column. On separate 3x5 cards, write down numbers that will later be associated with the foreman who will be doing the sampling. You will need two cards for each person since they will audit twice per day. Arrange the cards in random order and assign them to time slots on the schedule. At the end you will have created a daily random arrangement for the sampling process. By using a separate spreadsheet for each day of the week you can assure yourself that you will be building a random sample plan for the five days in the week. This may take a little time but make sure that the distribution is random and that samples are taken for every time slot during the week. Once you are satisfied that you have developed the random schedule, you are not finished. Remember, you were only arranging numbers, not actual names. Next, randomly match the foremen's names with the numbers. This eliminates bias since you do not know in advance which foreman has which number. Now you are finished. Save your materials since you will need them for subsequent weeks of the sampling effort.

Certainly there are other ways to establish a random daily schedule. Feel free to employ your own methods but be careful. It is important that the foremen make random samples so that you obtain good data.

2.7 Description of the Training Process

A flawless effort is possible but only with adequate training. It is important that everyone, especially those immediately involved, know exactly what they are to do and how to do it.

The training program as described in the lesson plan which follows should not last more than one hour and should be conducted the week prior to the initiation of the actual survey. This allows for the training to be closely coupled with the actual process minimizing any problems or confusion.

The training should be "kicked off" by the site manager. It is vitally important for ultimate success that everyone knows that the manager is in total support of the effort and expects the team to complete it with timely and accurate information. This is also the time to stress that the goal is to identify problems and fix them, not punish people for telling the truth. The balance of the training must be conducted by the site champion. In this way the work effort is started with a clear understanding of who is the project manager and who they can go to for problem resolution.

Training Lesson Plan

Topic	Time (min.)	Discussion
Agenda Review	5	• What the training will address so that the work sampling project can be a success
Work Sampling – What it is and what it is not.	5	• Recognition of the possible past problems with this type of effort • To clear up misconceptions • To begin developing an understanding of what the work effort is all about • Explain and reinforce that it is not designed to find people problems. It is process problem focused.
Why Are We Doing It?	5	• Overall productivity baseline data and future periodic reviews • An understanding of productivity problems to be addressed—process, not people
Discussion of a Valid Sample	5	• Stress honesty. This is a very critical success factor for this effort • Also, timeliness of data submission

(Continued)

Sampling Procedure	10	• Discussion of how the sampling procedure works. It is important that those to be sampled understand what to do and when to do it. • Identify who will be making the foremen contacts and where to submit the forms—the coordinator • Problems and what to do about them (see section 3.3)
Direct Category	5	• Review all definitions for understanding so that observations are accurate
Indirect Category	5	• Same as direct
Non-Productive Category	5	• Same as direct
Questions	15	
Close by site lead if possible		• Make sure they know who to call for help

Chapter 3: The Execution Phase

3.1 Sampling Methodology

The sampling process is easy. You already completed your random sample schedule in the planning phase. Now it is time to put it to use. Since the work crew's foreman is the person who will be sampling, he will need advance notice so that he can initiate the process during his assigned time slot. This is accomplished by the coordinator who contacts the foreman about ten minutes before his sample period. This provides the foreman with time to prepare to sample but still upholds the concept of randomness.

Once contacted, the foreman finds the members of his crew (this may require him to go to multiple locations) and he identifies on the sampling sheet what the individuals were doing at the moment they were observed. This "point-in-time" record of activity is exactly what we are trying to capture.

The process is concluded at the end of the day when the sampling sheets are turned into the coordinator so that the data can be entered onto the spreadsheet recording the total sampling effort's data.

3.2 Rules for Work Sampling

The purpose of work sampling as stated previously is to provide a snapshot of workforce productivity throughout the day. Therefore the rules for this effort are relatively simple and few:

1. Be open and honest with the input. Stating that someone is

productive when they are not invalidates the total effort.

2. No names! The samples are anonymous. All that gets entered onto the sampling card is the number of people performing in each category. There must be no connection with any individual and what they were doing during sampling.

3. Sample when asked. The random schedule is designed to capture productivity data throughout the day. Failure to sample in the assigned time frame skews the data.

4. Address questions raised by the workforce if you know the answer. If you don't know the answer, find out and communicate it. It is important that those being sampled are clear on the intent of the effort and what will be done with the results.

5. Turn in the sample cards at the end of the day.

3.3 Typical Problems and What to Do About Them

There are a number of typical problems which arise during the process of conducting a sampling activity in which you have many foremen surveying over an extended period of time. The list that follows is not all inclusive but it identifies and answers many of the typical problems which arise. These should be discussed during training.

- **The sampler is at a meeting.** The coordinator should substitute another foreman into the time slot and have the foreman at the meeting survey at another time. Knowing the department's meeting schedule when the random sample schedule is being prepared can help to eliminate this issue.

- **The sampler can't be reached via radio, pager, or phone.** The solution is the same as above except the coordinator will need to contact the foreman's supervisor and find out how to make contact when the foreman is next due to sample.

- **The foreman can't find all mechanics.** In this case those that couldn't be found during the sampling period should be listed as "number not observed." There is a space provided for this on the form. This will be further discussed later in this section under Process Monitoring. Nonobservable personnel are not a problem if it is within 10% of the total sample. A percent higher than this could indicate that the geographical area the foreman covering is too great for a full survey in a fifteen-minute time slot and needs to be addressed.

- **In the monitoring process (reviewing the results) it is felt that the productivity percent is too high.** This is usually based on a "gut" feeling because the site probably does not have previous samples. If this is the case you should use the data and focus on the indirect and non-productive areas for improvement. I believe that it is impossible for the entire group of foreman over a very large sample population to knowingly and collectively distort the data.

- **Obvious bad answers.** Call and discuss the answers with the foreman involved. This should be done in order to seek clarification, not to confront the foreman about the answers.

- **Who should attend the training?** All foremen and any potential move-up foremen (hourly mechanics who work up in foremen's job during vacation, etc.) so that everyone hears the same information. If someone is out sick or otherwise unavailable the site champion should provide training when they return.

- **Who should receive communications about the purpose of the effort and what will be done with the results?** Everyone should know what is happening!

- **When do you make up the random foreman survey sheets and what do you do with them?** The random survey schedule should be prepared a week in advance. The reason is that resource availability can change and preparing these schedules too far in advance is going to require rework to address these changes. In addition they should be kept confidential so that the foremen do not know their survey time until just prior.
- **The coordinator is out or not available.** As part of the process, a backup coordinator should be trained.
- **The foremen do not want to participate or possibly refuse.** This is a site issue. If the training is done properly then the foremen should not feel threatened. This is also an area where you can help by indicating that you will collect the data and destroy the sampling sheets after data entry.
- **Union issues.** This is also a site issue. Again this problem can be mitigated if there is upfront communication and the union understands the purpose of the effort. Another possible way to minimize this problem is to provide upfront training and a private presentation of the results to the union representatives at conclusion of the effort.

3.4 Process Monitoring

It is important to monitor the process as you proceed. This should be handled by the site champion. You do not want to wait until the end (possibly three weeks or more after the start) to have some understanding that everything was not going well. Therefore you need to require the data sheets daily. With the data being sent with this frequency, you can examine the input forms and address reporting problems within the next day. Handling the data in this fashion will also enable you to contact the foremen with any questions while the information is still fresh in the minds of those who observed it.

Another way to assess the health of the process is to load the data into the database and examine anything that possibly looks out of the range of expected results. For example, if the work crew begins their day at 7:00 a.m. it probably is not reasonable to expect that they would have a large percentage of their time in the working category. If you encountered data that showed people in the working category in this time period it would at least raise a flag for review of the process.

Last but not least, face-to-face dialogue with those performing the sampling will reveal a great deal about the health of the process. This activity is encouraged not only for the site champion but also for those on the management team who need to visibly show support. What better way to accomplish this than by asking those involved about the effort?

Chapter 4: The Results Phase

4.1 What Do You Do With the Data?

It is an irrefutable fact that work sampling unto itself is a worthless exercise! The real important part of the effort is what you do with the data you have acquired. If you have conducted the sampling process correctly you have in your possession somewhere between 2000 and 5000 data elements. When properly captured in a spreadsheet format they are going to tell you a story about the productivity of your workforce that is a statistically accurate representation of real life.

So the first question that you need to have answered is, how do you capture the data? For the purpose of our discussion we should assume that all work that is being measured is maintenance related. Many maintenance crews also perform capital jobs but you don't want to mix them or else you will wind up with skewed data. The reason is that capital jobs are usually well planned and continue over an extended period of time. As a result, the productivity is often higher than your typical maintenance tasks. Combining this data with maintenance work which is more discontinuous would certainly provide a false measure of productivity. The more capital work that is included in the sample the less value you will obtain from the study.

The first step in data capture is to build a spreadsheet for each day in which the sampling was conducted. Across the top you will have your fifteen-minute time increments and down the left column the result categories. The cell that corresponds to the time and sample category where data was measured is where you enter the totals for the day for that time increment and that category. The table below is a partial representation of what this would look like after a day's data was entered.

Example
Monday, Month/Day

	7:00– 7:15	**7:15– 7:30**	**7:30– 7:45**	**7:45– 8:00**	**8:00– 8:15**	**8:15– 8:30**	**8:30– 9:00**	**9:00– 9:15**
Working			6	5	6	7	6	
Planning			2	1		2		
Rec. Instruction		3	2	2				
Job Safety		3						
Handle Tools				1	1		1	
Handle Matl.				1	1		1	
Handle Equip.					2	1		
Clean Up							2	
Wait Tools								
Wait Material								
Wait Permit	3	2						
Wait Other								
Travel	5	2						10
Lost Time	2							

You will need a spreadsheet of this type for each day of the work sampling activity. This effort can be simplified using Microsoft Excel but if necessary it can be done on paper.

The next step is to add up the numbers in each cell for the entire sampling period so that you have a total for each time slot and each sampling category on one spreadsheet. This is where you are going to draw the data for your productivity charts.

4.2 The Work Sampling Charts

With the data you have in your possession there is a wide variety of charts that can be created. What you create depends on several things:

- How do you want to portray the results of the effort?
- What does management want to see?
- Where do you see problem areas that need to be highlighted for corrective action?

Each of these questions will focus your charting efforts. However, to get you started here are some ideas (there is a sample of each of these in Appendix 3):

Chart Title	**Information Provided**
Direct	This chart shows direct (both categories) as it changes throughout the day. It provides you with information about actual on-the-job productive time and shows where improvement is needed.
Indirect	This chart shows indirect (all categories) as it changes throughout the day. A high percentage in any one time period is a flag for you to look deeper into the reasons.
Non-Productive	This chart shows non-productive time (all categories) as it changes throughout the day. A goal of the measurement effort is to see where the organization is not being productive and determine how this can be improved.

(Continued)

Samples – Over Project Life	This chart shows total samples over the project life—to make sure you have enough information to have statistically accurate data and the correct number of samples per day. Checking the samples per day indicates if there are an equal number of samples being taken.
Samples – Per Period of the Day	This chart shows the number of total samples for each period of the day. If your random selection process is working correctly there should be consistency in the numbers of samples taken at each time increment throughout the day. A low number of samples in a specific period should be addressed.

The above table is only a partial list. From having been involved throughout the process you will be able to develop other charts that, if required, better suit your needs.

4.3 Additional Views

There are other ways to view the data such as, by work group, by craft, by operations/production area, or even by shop vs. field work. While these can provide valuable information, the problem is that by filtering in this manner you reduce the number of samples in the data set and as the number gets lower so does the level of statistical accuracy. My suggestion if you wish to get this granular is to read Chapter 6 and focus your efforts on the spot audit approach.

4.4 Now That You Have the Data, What's Next?

From the charts and the data that you have acquired there will be some obvious areas that you will recognize as needing improvement. Other areas will also become obvious as you do further and more detailed analysis.

As these areas are identified you need more information about the problem in order to determine what corrective actions need to be applied. This is accomplished by doing Root Cause Failure Analysis. The basic process simply involves asking "why" a number of times until you feel that you have gotten to the root of the problem. At this point you can develop your corrective action plan, and by repairing the root you can essentially solve the problem. For this process to work optimally, you will need a small work team. The reason there is a need for a team is that a single person's solution may not always take into account all of the aspects of the problem. This team needs to be open and honest about the root causes of the problem being addressed otherwise it will never be corrected.

Let's look at an example so that the process is clear:

Suppose that one of the problems apparent from the work sampling study is that the crews spend excessive time waiting for permits. If the team asks themselves why this occurs they may arrive at several possible reasons. For example:

1. The operators did not know the job was scheduled.
2. The operators resist writing permits until the crew shows up to do the work.
3. The operators have other preassigned tasks at the start of the shift and no time for permit preparation.
4. The operators do not care.

There may be other ideas but the four listed will suffice for our example. Next, the items are ranked as: 1 = unlikely, 3 = maybe likely, and 5 = most likely. This allows ideas like "the operators are not interested" to be eliminated. Suppose the one item that scores a 5 is "the operators did not know the job was scheduled." The next step in the process is to ask why they didn't know. This generates another list and you go through the same process once again. This effort continues until you reach what you believe is the root of the problem. Solving the root usually solves the issue. For this example the root cause of the productivity problem was that the production supervisors had been told not to include maintenance work that was scheduled on their end-of-shift reports. This change was implemented because in the past it had cluttered up the report with extraneous information that they did not feel was necessary. Consequently the operators did not know what work was scheduled and could not prepare the permits in advance. Once this was corrected the permit issue resolved itself.

Obviously this is a simplified example; however, the process is what is needed to identify and develop corrective actions for the root causes of the productivity problems that were identified in the work sampling study.

4.5 Now That You Understand the Roots, What's Next?

Just as having the data and not acting on it is a poor idea so is having the solution and not implementing it. The team you have assembled to review the data and conduct the Root Cause Analysis is also there for another purpose. They need to be the team who develop and implement the corrective actions designed to improve areas of low productivity. One last comment, implementation is wonderful but you also need to audit to make certain that the corrective actions that were put into place are working and driving benefits. That is where resampling comes into play.

Chapter 5: The Continuous Improvement Phase

5.1 Over and Over Again

Work sampling is not a one-time event! The initial sampling is your baseline or starting point for a long-term value-adding journey. Once you have your baseline data, have identified the barriers, and put in place initiatives aimed at barrier elimination, it is time to check up and see if the initiatives that you have put into place have improved productivity. The way this is done, of course, is by conducting another sampling and comparing the results with the baseline. If your initiatives have worked and improved productivity, the proof will be in the results obtained from subsequent surveys.

5.2 When To Resample

The answer to this question is that you want to resample, not too soon, but not too late. If you resample too soon the productivity initiatives will not have had a chance to take hold. If you resample too late you may miss problems that should be addressed and may be eroding your efforts. That is why resampling is a site-specific issue because more than anyone else, you will know when the time is right.

Once you do the initial resample you also need to set up a future frequency so that this becomes a process of continuous improvement, not one that has to be justified each time resampling is scheduled.

At some point you may want to adjust the frequency or even discontinue the effort because you are no longer seeing across-the-board improvement. However, I would suspect that there are specific areas that, in spite of improvement elsewhere, never seem to get any better. An example of these might be the productivity level at the start of the shift or just after lunch. In these cases you need to focus your sampling efforts through a process called spot sampling which is addressed in Chapter 6.

Chapter 6: Spot Sampling

6.1 Spot Sampling

Spot sampling is somewhat different from the productivity sampling we have been discussing in the first five chapters of this book. Spot sampling is just what the name implies; instead of sampling the entire day, it is a sample of a single time period, usually the first job of the day or other time periods where you feel productivity issues exist. I recommend you start with the first job of the day.

Why the first job? The answer is rather simple. Hopefully the work for the coming day is planned and coordinated in advance so that when the workers arrive, the foremen can send them off to the first job with minimal loss of time. The productivity problems arise when this job is not ready and the workers go into "standby" mode. Usually this causes frustration and the day's productivity goes downhill from there.

The purpose of spot sampling is to gauge the overall effectiveness of the communication, coordination, and cooperation between Maintenance and Production to successfully begin each day's productive work. As barriers identified in this process are eliminated, the spot audits should indicate that these jobs are proceeding more effectively and efficiently, ensuring safe, timely starts, prompt permitting, readily available tools and parts, a prepared crew, and a more trusting working relationship between the involved organizations.

While spot sampling tends to be most effective related to the first job of the day, it can also be used for other time periods where productivity problems exist. It is also another way for you to analyze a specific problematic time period identified in the work sampling effort. This process can also be applied by small organizations that do not have sufficient managerial staff or a workforce large enough for the full-blown work sampling initiative.

6.2 Site Commitment and the Spot Audit Team

Just as with the work sampling process, site commitment, open and honest communication, and training are required. However, we are going to conduct spot audits for all of the work crews on a daily basis, therefore this effort has a different set of requirements:

- It will take about one hour of a person's time daily.
- The foremen are getting the work crews out to the jobs so they will not be part of the audit group.
- The auditor team will be drawn from an extended site management list across multiple departments.
- If possible, each work crew will have a job audit in the designated time period. This will require more than one auditor each day. Resource availability may require that this plan be altered.
- Jobs of "medium-to-high" complexity should be audited to expose the work barriers. "Low" complexity jobs should be avoided if possible.
- The process is much more detailed in that we are looking for barriers to productivity on specific jobs in a specific time period, not generalized categories.
- The process is also much more interactive since those doing the auditing don't know the job and need to discuss it (and the associated barriers) with the work crew and the production team who own the equipment.

- There is no defined end point for this effort. The auditing will continue until the identified barriers are eliminated and a productivity increase is noted.

To accomplish the spot audit process we will need a large team which will be drawn from interdepartmental refinery management representatives who will be assigned to this task. Our goal will be to make the list large enough so that a single team member will only survey one week (all five days) every other month. This time requirement may be less if additional resources are available. The audit duration will require approximately one hour. This should be a manageable time commitment for the team members.

6.3 Resource Requirements

There are two levels of resources required for this effort:

- **The Coordinator** – While the coordinator for the work sampling effort can be anyone in the organization, usually someone in a clerical capacity, this is not the case for spot audits. The coordinator in this case needs to understand the work. It makes little sense to send a spot auditor out to view a two man fifteen-minute job. For work of this sort very little insight to work productivity barriers will be revealed. For this reason the coordinator needs to understand the work and send the spot auditors to review jobs from medium-to-high complexity. It is also important for the coordinator to understand the work since they will be doing the initial analysis.

- **The Auditors** – In order to engage a large segment of the management team and reduce the individual time burden, the auditor group will be rather large. The people in the auditor resource pool also need to have some minimal level of understanding of the work so that they can recognize barriers.

This will also enable them to intelligently conduct a work discussion with the maintenance crew.

6.4 The Process

The spot audit process is rather simple but will reveal a great deal of important information. It consists of five steps as follows:

Step 1 – The evening prior to the audit, the auditor (there will be more than one person per day if you wish to audit multiple jobs) will meet with the person coordinating the effort to determine which job they will audit the next day.

Step 2 – Fifteen minutes prior to the start time for the mechanics, the auditor will arrive at the job site or in some cases the control room responsible for the work site. They will identify themselves to the operators as a "spot auditor." They will ascertain that the permits (if required) have been written and the equipment is prepared for maintenance.

Step 3 – When the work crew arrives the time will be noted and the auditor will identify themselves to the crew. It is important that prior communication has been made to the entire organization so that the crew does not view the audit as a threat. The purpose in communicating with the crew is to help the auditor understand the job and recognize the barriers that the crew confronts in order to perform the work.

Step 4 – The auditor will then visit the job site and complete the spot audit form located in the appendix. Pertinent questions can and should be addressed to the foreman and the workers to obtain accurate information. There is also a section on the form for the auditor to identify barriers that they saw which prohibited the work from proceeding in a smooth and efficient manner.

Step 5 – When the audit is finished, the auditor will complete and submit the spot audit form to the coordinator for analysis of the data.

6.5 Action Items/Analysis

Conducting audits without subsequent analysis and action items to improve the process is worthless. As the audit forms are submitted they need to be recorded and analyzed to identify barriers and improvement areas. The process to accomplish this task can mirror the process described for the productivity analysis in Chapter 4, section 4.4. As with any initiative of this sort, measurements are also required. This will enable you to determine if the improvements put in place as a result of the effort are adding value and improving productivity.

From the Author

It is true that sampling in order to measure workforce productivity takes time, effort, and commitment. I hope that you recognize that conducting this work internally is not as difficult as you might have imagined when the topic was first discussed. Additionally, since you will be doing the sampling on a periodic basis, the internal approach is low-to-no cost, making a continued effort of this sort palatable to the management team.

Hopefully this text has proven this point and sparked your interest in conducting a workforce productivity initiative of your own. Remember the initial question that I asked at the beginning: "Why would you undertake any work improvement initiative if you had no way to measure the results?" You wouldn't, yet this approach to maintenance improvement is done every day. Productivity measurement provides the measurement tool you need and will help you add measureable business value.

Feel free to contact me if you need additional information or support.

Steve Thomas

E-mail: changemgt999@yahoo.com

Appendix

1. Work Sampling Form*
2. Spot Audit Form*
3. Sample Charts
    3.1 Direct Work Sample Chart
    3.2 Indirect Work Sample Chart
    3.3 Non-Productive Sample Chart
    3.4 Sample Count Chart
    3.5 Samples Per Period

(*Note: All forms are samples and should be modified to suit the work and site involved in the process.)

Appendix 1 – Work Sampling Form

Name:			
Date:		Day of Week:	
Number in Crew:		Number Not Observed:	
Scheduled Time Slot	From:	To:	
Enter the number of people that fit each category when you make your observation. No names just the count of the mechanics that fit each of the respective categories.			

Direct Work	Working	
	Planning	
Indirect Work	Receiving Instructions	
	Job Safety Issues	
	Handling Tools	
	Handling Materials	
	Handling Equipment	
	Clean Up	
Non Productive	Waiting Tools	
	Waiting Material	
	Waiting Permits	
	Waiting Other	
	Traveling	
	Lost Time	

Appendix 2 - Spot Audit Form

Name:	
Day/Date:	**Scheduled Start Time:**
Work Area:	**Equipment ID:**
Work Order #:	**Number in Crew:**
Description of Work:	

Pre-Job Audit Information

Was the Production/Operations group aware of the job?	**Yes**	**No**	**NA**
If a permit is required for the job, was it prepared?	**Yes**	**No**	**NA**
Was the equipment prepared for work by Maintenance?	**Yes**	**No**	**NA**
Was the work area clean and ready for the work to begin?	**Yes**	**No**	**NA**
If lock-out/tag-out was required, has it been completed?	**Yes**	**No**	**NA**
If pipe blinding is required are the blinds identified?	**Yes**	**No**	**NA**

Spot Audit Information

Did the work start on time?	**Yes**	**No**	**NA**
Did the mechanics understand the job when they arrived?	**Yes**	**No**	**NA**
Did the work crew have a work order in their possession?	**Yes**	**No**	**NA**
Did the workers bring the required tools?	**Yes**	**No**	**NA**
Did the workers bring the required materials?	**Yes**	**No**	**NA**
Was the necessary equipment (hi-reach, crane, etc.) on site?	**Yes**	**No**	**NA**
Did the foreman check on the job while you were there?	**Yes**	**No**	**NA**
Did the work crew size seem reasonable for the job?	**Yes**	**No**	**NA**

Barriers to Work Execution (check those that apply)

		Notes:
Safety Issues	☐	
Obtaining Permits	☐	
Equipment Preparation	☐	
Understanding Job Requirements	☐	
Material Availability	☐	
Tool Availability	☐	
Support Equipment Availability	☐	
Poor Planning	☐	
Poor Work Direction	☐	
Lack of Skill	☐	
Other -	☐	
Other -	☐	

Appendix 3 – Sample Charts

Appendix 3.1 – Direct Work Sample Chart

This chart shows the percent of direct observations over the work day. It represents a standard eight-hour day from 7:00 a.m. to 3:30 p.m. with a morning and afternoon break and an unpaid lunch from 12:00 to 12:30. Notice the fall-off in direct working time prior to both breaks and at the end of the day. There is also an early break for lunch and a slow return—all areas for improvement in productivity. Note that the total percent for the direct, indirect, and non-productive charts should equal 100%.

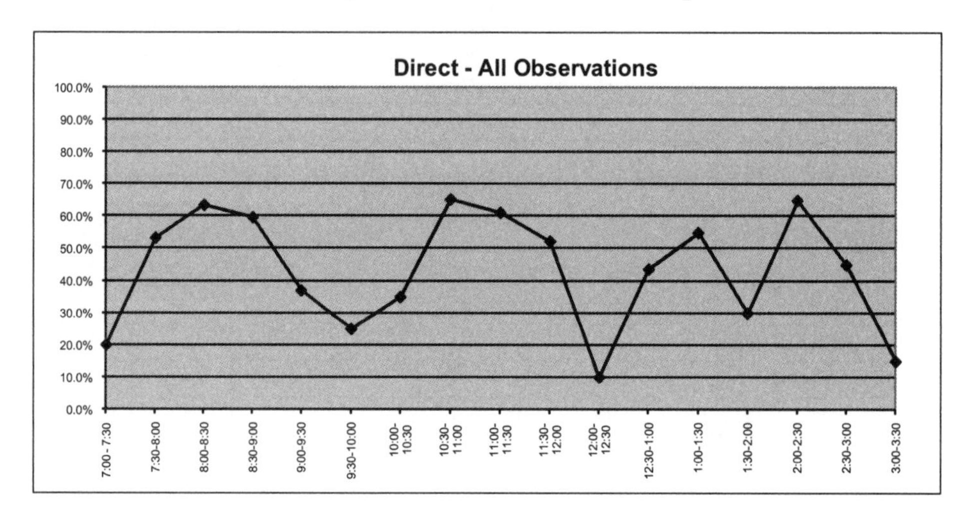

Appendix 3.2 – Indirect Work Sample Chart

This chart shows the percent of indirect observations over the work day. Note the high indirect percentage as the workforce prepares for the day's work. Also note the expected drop-off around breaks and lunch.

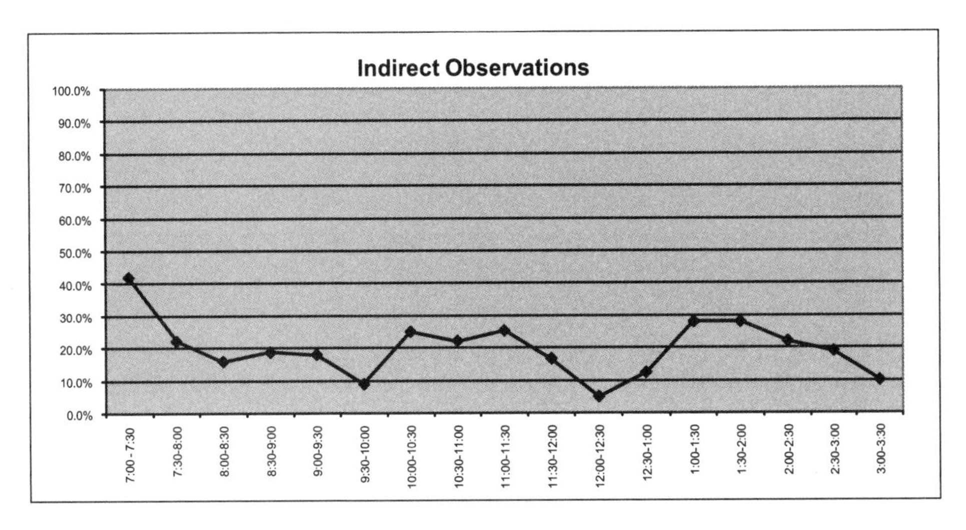

Appendix 3.3 – Non-Productive Sample Chart

This chart shows the percent of non-productive observations over the work day. It is exactly opposite from the direct chart showing the large percentages of non-productive time around breaks, lunch and early quit time. As you can see in this example the problem is the slow start and slowdown at break and at the end of the day.

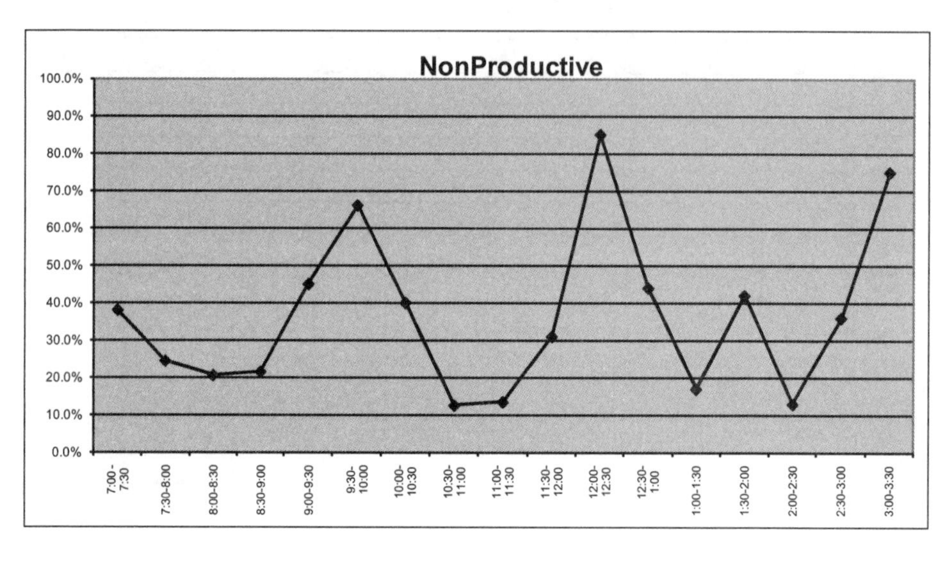

Appendix 3.4 – Sample Count Chart (shows number per day and cumulative)

This chart shows sample counts. It is useful to show that the sample counts were uniform across the work days of the sample. If this is not the case you can add additional sampling in the time slots where the count is low. It also shows that the total samples for statistical accuracy have been attained.

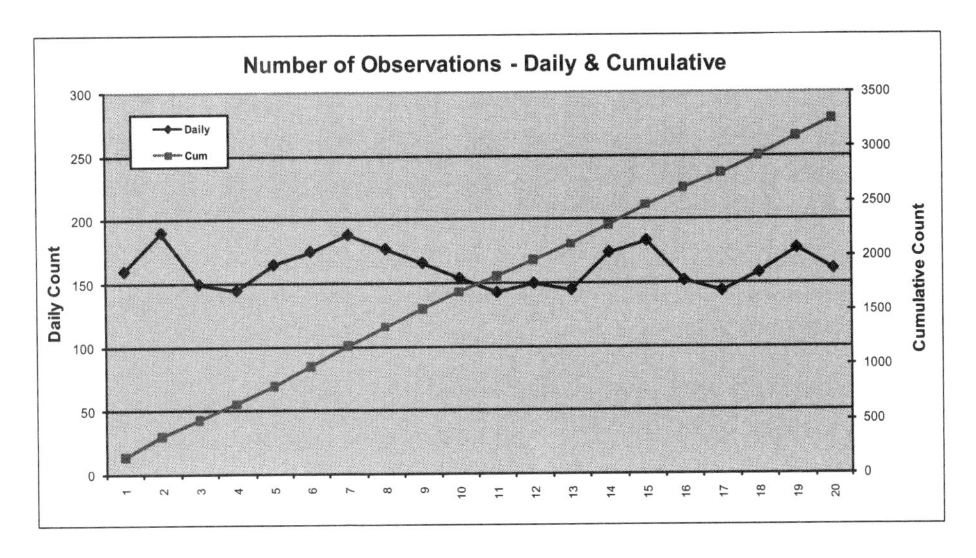

Appendix 3.5 – Samples per Period

This chart is similar to 3.4 but only shows the count per work period.

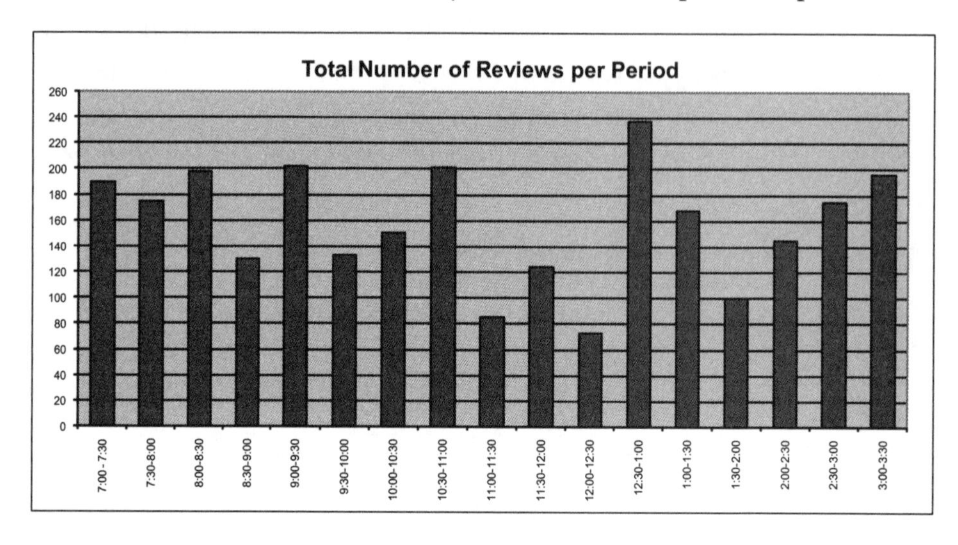

BIBLIOGRAPHY

E.I. du Pont de Nemours and Company, *Maintenance Work Sampling*, n.p., n.d.

L. Lapin, *Probability And Statistics For Modern Engineering Second Edition: The Statistical Sampling Study*, Belmont, CA: Duxbury Press, p. 242-256.

R. M. Barnes, *Work Sampling – Second Edition: Procedure For Making A Work Sampling Study*, Los Angeles, CA: University of California, p. 63-67.

Trotter & Associates, Inc., *Workforce Utilization Analysis*, n.p., n.d.

Thomas, Stephen J., *Successfully Managing Change In Organizations: A Users Guide*, New York, NY: Industrial Press, 2001.

Thomas, Stephen J., *Improving Maintenance And Reliability Through Cultural Change*, New York, NY: Industrial Press, 2005.

About the Author

Stephen J. Thomas has 40 years of refinery maintenance and reliability experience. Through personal involvement at all levels of the work process, he has gained vast experience including conducting workforce productivity sampling during daily maintenance and turnaround projects. Coupled with a B.S. in Electrical Engineering from Drexel University and M.S. degrees in both Systems Engineering and Organizational Dynamics from the University of Pennsylvania, this experience has enabled him to add significant value to the many projects on which he has worked.